HUGO AND THE SPACEDOG

LEE LORENZ

Prentice-Hall, Inc./Englewood Cliffs, New Jersey

For Speagle,
the earth dog

Printed in the United States of America ·J
Prentice-Hall International, Inc., London
Prentice-Hall of Australia, Pty. Ltd., Sydney
Prentice-Hall Canada, Inc., Toronto
Prentice-Hall of India Private Ltd., New Delhi
Prentice-Hall of Japan, Inc., Tokyo
Prentice-Hall of Southeast Asia Pte. Ltd., Singapore
Whitehall Books Limited, Wellington, New Zealand
Editora Prentice-Hall Do Brasil LTDA., Rio de Janeiro

10 9 8 7 6 5 4 3 2 1

Library of Congress Cataloging in Publication Data
Lorenz, Lee.
    Hugo and the spacedog.
    Summary: A wandering dog is refused a watchpost by the
farm animals until a space visitor proves the need for a watchdog.
    [1. Dogs—Fiction.   2. Domestic animals—Fiction.
3. Space vehicles—Fiction.   4. Extraterrestrial beings—
Fiction]   I. Title.
PZ7.L884Hu   1983   [E]   82-22960
ISBN 0-13-444497-3

Hugo was a wanderer. He loved to travel through the open country and sleep under the star-filled sky.

One morning he awoke and looked down on the prettiest little farm he had ever seen.

"Perhaps it's time to stop travelling and settle down," he thought. "This looks like a wonderful place to stay."

Hugo walked down the hill to the farm. He met a horse grazing in the meadow.

"Good morning," said Hugo. "This is certainly a nice farm. I would like to live here."

"Our farm *is* nice," said the horse, "but everyone who lives here must earn his keep."

"For example," the horse continued, "our cow gives milk."
"I can't do that," said Hugo.

"I myself pull this plow," said the horse.
"I'm not strong enough to do that," said Hugo.

"And our chicken lays eggs."
"Well, I certainly can't do that," said Hugo.

"And to clean up after everybody," the horse went on, "here is our goat."

"Sorry, but that is not for me," said Hugo.

"Well, what *can* you do?" asked the horse.

"I can't do any of those things," answered Hugo, "but I can do something no one else can do. I can be a watchdog!"

All the animals started laughing. "A watchdog! We don't need a watchdog. You'd better try somewhere else."

Hugo climbed slowly back to the top of the hill. "I guess I'll always be a wanderer," he sighed. And all night Hugo sat there, gazing at the stars.

Suddenly, as dawn approached, something shot past Hugo and crashed in a shower of flames behind the barn.

He raced down the hill. "Wake up, wake up!" he cried, "Fire! Fire!"

The animals ran wildly in every direction, scooping up water and throwing it at the flames.

"You can't put out a fire that way!" shouted Hugo. "Each of you get a bucket. I'll fill them as you pass them back and forth."

The animals agreed.

So with Hugo at the pump, they worked together and swiftly put out the fire.

As the smoke cleared, they could see a strange-looking craft sitting in the middle of the duck pond.

"Look!" cried the duck. "What is that?"

"Why, it's a spaceship," said Hugo.

Then, as they all watched in amazement, a small door opened and a mysterious-looking figure appeared.

The animals were afraid. They ran and hid—all except Hugo, who stepped forward and asked, "Who are you?"

"I am a wanderer from a distant planet. My name is XrRypllth."

"I can't pronounce that," said Hugo. "So if you don't mind, I'll just call you Spacedog. But why are you here?"

"Well, after many years of travelling around the universe, I grew homesick. I was headed for my own planet when a meteor hit my ship and knocked it off course. I ran out of fuel and had to land here.

"I'm sorry I've made such a mess, but I need fuel for my ship so that I can get back home."

"Well, right now," said the duck, "you're sitting in the middle of *my* pond."

She tried to push the spaceship, but she slipped and fell over in the mud.

"That isn't the way to do it," said Hugo. "If we put a rope around the ship and all pull together, I'll bet we can pull it out."

"The sooner the better," muttered the duck, wiping herself off.

They all thought this was a good idea, so they tied a long rope around the spaceship.

"One, two, three, *pull*!" called Hugo, as they slowly hauled it out of the pond.

"Now, then, Spacedog," Hugo asked, "what kind of fuel do you need?"

"This ship will run on almost anything," replied the spacedog.

"How about apples?" asked the pig. "Nothing like a fresh apple to get *me* started."

So they loaded the fuel tank with apples.

The spacedog tried the engine. It sputtered and burped and shot out a stream of applesauce, but the ship only rose a few feet into the air and fell back to earth.

"How about oats?" asked the horse. "A great pile of oats gets me going in no time."
So they filled the tank with oats.

The engine coughed and wheezed and spilled out a big puddle of oatmeal, but still the ship barely rose above the treetops.

"What about corn?" asked the hen. "Everybody knows there is lots of energy in corn."

So they stuffed the fuel tank with corn.

This time the ship sputtered and shook and rose straight up as the engine shot out a great shower of popcorn. In a few seconds, however, it settled back on the ground. The spacedog looked discouraged.

"I have an idea," said Hugo. "We put out the fire when we worked together, and we moved the spacecraft when we worked together. If we mix everything together, I'll bet the ship will fly just fine."

"It makes sense to me," said the cow.

"Great idea," said the pig.

"Let's do it," said the chicken.

So they dragged over a large tub and filled it with apples, oats, corn, and a few other things as well.

Then they climbed into the tub and jumped up and down on the mixture until it was smooth as cream.

"This should do it," said Hugo, as they poured the mixture into the fuel tank. "Good luck to you, Spacedog."

"Thank you, my friends," replied XrRypllth. "Perhaps one day we will meet again."

Then they all held their ears as the spacedog started the engine.

With a roar and a burst of flame, the spaceship shot into the sky.
"It worked!" shouted the animals. "Hurray for Hugo!"
The spaceship circled the farm, then disappeared beyond the clouds.

"Well," said the horse, "I hope you will stay with us, Hugo. You've proved that we really do need a watchdog."

"Yes, please stay," the animals all shouted together.

"Of course," said Hugo. "I was hoping you would ask."

So Hugo stopped wandering and lived on the farm. The animals built him a little guardhouse on the hilltop. And every night he climbs up there and watches over the farm, halfway between his friend in the sky and his friends in the valley below.